JIDE AND PETRA ARE TWO NORMAL HUMAN KIDS FROM PLANET EARTH, BUT THEY'RE ABOUT TO DEPART ON AN INTERGALACTIC JOURNEY ... AN ADVENTURE THROUGH

SPACE-TIME!

AND SO TOBEY (AND TOBEY AND TOBEY, WHO ARE CLONES OF TOBEY, BECAUSE THEIR ENTIRE ALIEN CIVILIZATION IS MADE OF TOBEY CLONES), SHARED ADVANCED TECHNOLOGY WITH THE PEOPLE OF EARTH.

Soon, humans will be ready to participate in the most advanced space exploration mission ever!

For Earth people, not for me.

And so you're going to pick the best, most experienced and popular astronauts to join you?

No, actually we're going to send half-trained kids.

Half?!

Don't worry. That half is the IMPORTANT half.

That's why I founded the Earth School for Space Mission Preparation. The human children attending E.S.S.M.P. will learn almost everything they need to know to go on this really cool journey and make you adults super jealous!

Er, that's great, Jide. We're going to finish the week with something fun.

Aren't tests fun?

Spaceships sometimes require repairs in conditions that would be deadly to astronauts.

Yeah, that sounds fun.

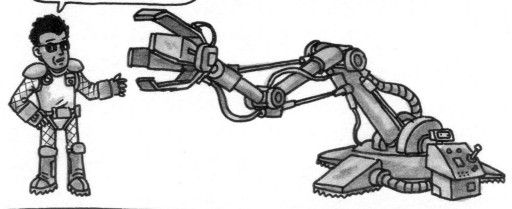

So you'll need to become experts at operating the Telescoping Claw Remote Robotic Arm.

We get to play with the T.C.R. robot arm? Sweet!

Nobody "plays" with a T.C.R. Robotic arm. It's too expensive for you to even touch. We're going on a field trip for a simulator exercise.

MEANWHILE, ON MARS...

INSIDE MARS BASE

Hey, kids! You're all ready? Great!

Kay, where's Tobey?

He's on Earth preparing the human astronauts who will join us here on Mars for the rest of the mission.

Choosing from all of the elite candidates will be difficult.

Until he's back, it's up to me to get you all to work.

It's also up to you when he is here.

Yeah. Tobey goofs off a lot.

WHAT'S NEXT FOR PETRA AND JIDE?
FIND OUT IN BOOK ONE:

LOGISTICAL MECHANIZED NEUROBOTIC TOOL

L.M.N.T.S (PRONOUNCED "ELEMENTS") ARE THE SMART ROBOTS THAT RUN THINGS ON THE SPACE-TIME! MISSION, FROM OPERATING SPACESHIPS TO MAKING SURE THINGS ON PLANETARY BASES RUN SMOOTHLY. SOME L.M.N.T.S ARE GENERAL SERVICE UNITS, WHILE OTHERS HAVE SPECIALTIES OR SPECIFIC JOBS SUCH AS MEDICAL, SECURITY, OR NAVIGATIONAL DUTIES. EACH L.M.N.T. IS UNIQUE, ALTHOUGH ALL ARE MODELED FROM A STANDARD DESIGN TEMPLATE.

DUB

PABLO

KAY

COBY

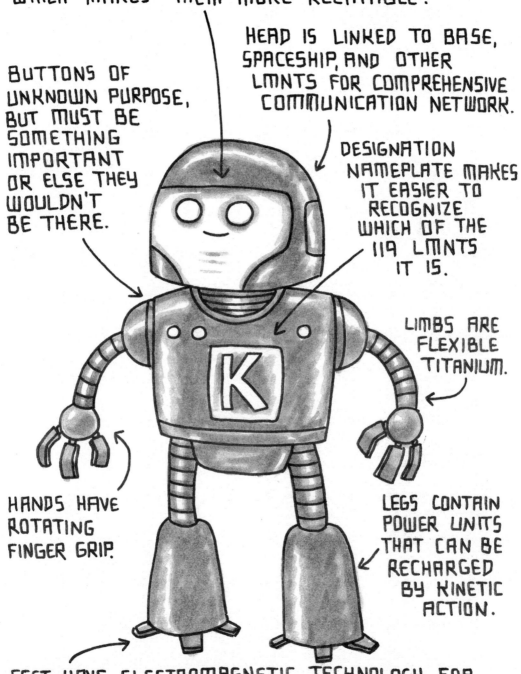

A BRIEF TRANSMISSION FROM THE AUTHOR

When I was a kid, I LOVED science fiction!

Star Wars, Star Trek, Dune...

I loved reading about extraterrestrial life and space travel.

My favorite UFO book when I was a kid →

I even had dreams about UFOs and aliens.

And I imagined what it'd be like if aliens really visited Earth!

That inspired me to write this story about the first aliens to contact Earth.

Enjoy!

INK-Jeff • Script-Brown • ~~Colur~~ Jeffrey B. • Artist-JeffB. • Letter-Jeff Brown • Color-Jeff Brown

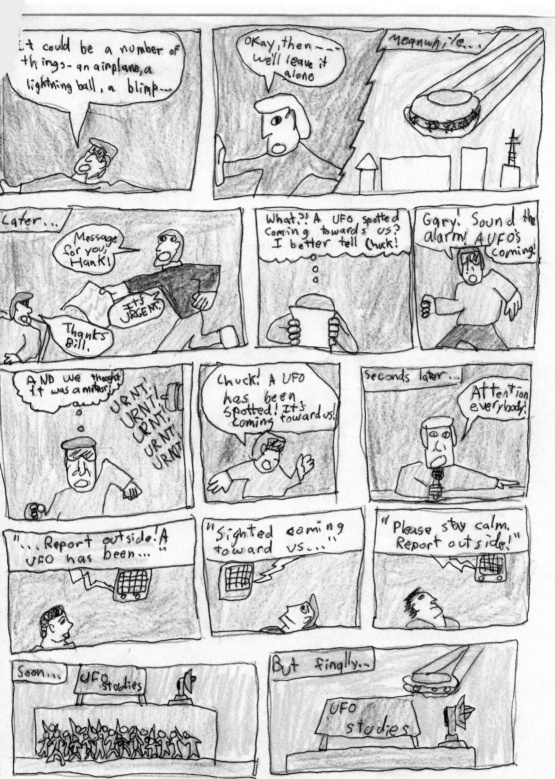